BALLOONING

BY C. H. GIBBS-SMITH

COMPANION ROYAL AERONAUTICAL SOCIETY

WITH THIRTY-TWO PLATES

PENGUIN BOOKS · LONDON

MCMXLVIII

THE KING PENGUIN BOOKS

EDITOR: N. B. L. PEVSNER · TECHNICAL EDITOR: R. B. FISHENDEN

PUBLISHED BY PENGUIN BOOKS LIMITED,

HARMONDSWORTH, MIDDLESEX, ENGLAND

AND BY PENGUIN BOOKS PTY, LTD, 200 NORMANBY ROAD,

MELBOURNE, AUSTRALIA

THIS BOOK
FIRST PUBLISHED
1948

TEXT PAGES PRINTED AT THE CURWEN PRESS, PLAISTOW
COLOUR PLATES MADE BY JOHN SWAIN AND SON, LTD, BARNET, HERTS
AND PRINTED BY BALDING AND MANSELL, WISBECH, CAMBS
COVER DESIGNED BY MARIAN MAHLER
MADE IN GREAT BRITAIN

AD ASTRA

Let Posterity know, and knowing be astonished, that on the 15th day of September 1784 Vincent Lunardi of Lucca in Tuscany, the First Aerial Traveller in Britain, mounting from the Artillery Ground in London and traversing the Regions of the Air for two Hours and fifteen Minutes, in this Spot revisited the Earth. On this rude monument for ages be recorded that wondrous Enterprise successfully achieved by the Powers of Chemistry and the Fortitude of Man, that Improvement in Science which the Great Author of all Knowledge, patronyzing by His Providence the Invention of Mankind hath graciously permitted to their Benefit and His own Eternal Glory.

INSCRIPTION
ON THE LUNARDI MONUMENT
AT STANDON, HERTS

TO CONSTANCE
BABINGTON SMITH

*

ACKNOWLEDGEMENTS

THE Author wishes to offer his thanks first and foremost to Mr J. E. Hodgson, balloonophile *en-chef* and the owner of the finest collection of ballooniana in England, for many kindnesses and especially for allowing him to reproduce eight of his prints; also to Capt. J. L. Pritchard, Secretary of the Royal Aeronautical Society; Col. J. L. Preston, Secretary-General of the Royal Aero Club; Mr M. J. B. Davy of the Science Museum; Lord Ventry; the National Geographic Society of Washington, D.C.; the Editor of the *Illustrated London News*; the Director of the Andrée Museum at Granna, Sweden; Major C. C. Turner; and Messrs Sampson Low, Marston & Company.

★

THE HODGSON-CUTHBERT
COLLECTION

IN 1917 Mr Hodgson bought the great collection of ballooning books and prints first started by John Cuthbert about 1820. Many additions have been made by Mr Hodgson and now (1948), through the generosity of Sir Frederick Handley Page, the whole collection has been presented to the Royal Aeronautical Society.

CONTENTS

FOREWORD   9

FAMOUS FLIGHTS   12

THE ANATOMY OF BALLOONING   33

A BALLOONING DATE LIST   38

A SHORT BOOK LIST   40

Text Illustrations

On the title-page: A Wedding trip in a balloon
    at New York: signing the marriage contract,
    1865. From a contemporary London wood-
    engraving

Fig. 1. Cocking's Parachute, 1837   9

Fig. 2. Lana's Aerial Ship, 1670   12

Fig. 3. Guzmão's Aerial Ship   13

Fig. 4. Diagram of a Balloon   32

Fig. 5. Dragging   37

PLATES 1–32

Fig. 1. Cocking's Parachute. 1837.

FOREWORD

THE history of ballooning is not a very profound study, but it is really excellent value. Ballooning produced the first of the world's air pilots, and, for more than a century before the triumph of powered flight, it fostered a tradition of skilful and courageous airmanship. It is to be regretted that most modern airmen have not the same acquaintance with the history and achievements of their craft as sailors have with theirs.

It doesn't pay to patronize the old-timers. It was they, both men and women, who learnt to know the air and its ways and who first made the world air-minded. It needed guts to travel into an unknown world, and then to work and strive after new machines, new techniques and new adventures. Any story which holds as much action and emotion as does the history of ballooning is well worth the telling.

It was the French who first 'enclosed a cloud in a bag' and so rose to 'bestride the lazy-pacing clouds and sail upon the bosom of the air'.

After Pilâtre de Rozier became the world's No. 1 air pilot in 1783, Europe went 'balloonatic' in a big way. Scientists, generals and showmen all tried to apply it to their jobs, and all managed to utilize balloons in some way. Then came the French Revolution and a general slump in European aeronautics. For more than a century the main appeal of balloons was as entertainment for those on the ground and a novel thrill for the few that went up as passengers. Many of the balloons of those days were gay affairs, with their pear-shaped envelopes and brightly coloured gores, and the crowds who thronged Cremorne Gardens, Vauxhall or the Crystal Palace got their money's worth with an occasional thrill thrown in. Often when delving into the records of ballooning one wonders why such obviously good entertainment as a firework display from the air, or even a plain ascent of a fine balloon, to say nothing of the other pleasures of Cremorne, are not revived today. Perhaps we are dull, self-conscious dogs; or too sophisticated; or just too lazy.

The showman was not the only exploiter of balloons in the last century. The scientist made good use of them for meteorological and other investigations and the small instrument-carrying weather balloon, first thought of in 1892, is an indispensable tool of modern science.

Napoleon's generals soon saw the possibilities of the tethered observation balloon and this, having served its turn, led through many incarnations to the barrage balloon of today. And then there was the airship, still not dead, which of course grew straight out of the balloon.

Apart from war, science and entertainment, there is the last and best application of the balloon—for sport, pure and simple. This was mainly due to the founding of the Aero Club in 1901, and a veritable balloon renaissance followed. It began to decline when the aeroplane looked like becoming a practical proposition (about 1909) and, except for the Gordon Bennett races, died when the Kaiser's War started.

Ballooning and gliding should stand to aeronautics as sailing does to the sea; gliding—silent aviation—is spreading throughout the world; one wonders if balloons—silent aerostation—will come into their own as a sporting escape from noise and neurosis. I cannot do better than quote a delightful passage from *Old Flying Days* by Major C. C. Turner.

'I am in a very small balloon over Surrey on the last day of a beautiful May. So light is the wind that on that little voyage three hours and a half were taken to travel sixteen miles, from Roehampton to Betchworth. There is scarcely a cloud in the sky ...

'Very slowly I approach a big wood. It would rather express the situation were I to say that very slowly a big wood comes nearer to the balloon, for there is no sense of movement, and the earth below seems to be moving slowly past a stationary balloon. As the wood comes nearer I watch the aneroid and get a bag of ballast ready. For I know that over the wood the air will be slightly cooler, with probably a slight down-draught due to convection, and that the balloon will immediately begin to descend; and I shall have to check that descent by throwing a little ballast.

'Fifteen hundred feet up and almost absolute silence, broken occasionally by the barking of a dog heard very faintly, or by a voice hailing the balloon, and by an occasional friendly creak of the basket and rigging if I move ever so slightly. Then quite suddenly I am aware of something new.

'The balloon has come down a little already, and I scatter a few handfuls of sand and await the certain result. But my attention is no longer on that, it is arrested by this new sound which I hear, surely the most wonderful and the sweetest sound heard by mortal ears. ... It is the combined singing of thousands of birds, of half the kinds which make the English spring so lovely. I do not hear one above the others; all are blended together in a wonderful harmony without change of pitch or tone, yet never wearying the ear.

'By very close attention I seem to be able at times to pick out an individual song. No doubt at all there are wrens, and chaffinches, and blackbirds and thrushes, hedge-sparrows, warblers, greenfinches, and bullfinches and a score of others, by the hundred; and their singing comes up to me from that ten-acre wood in one sweet volume of heavenly music.'

THE pre-history of balloons goes back to 1513 when Leonardo da Vinci, on the road to Rome for Pope Leo X's coronation, seems to have filled wafer-thin wax figures with hot air and made them fly. I say 'seems' because Vasari's account is tantalizingly slight and Leonardo's note-books say nothing.

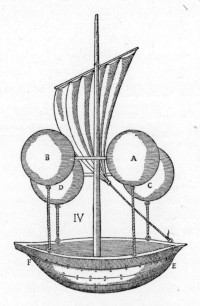

Fig. 2. Lana's Aerial Ship. 1670.

It was the Jesuit, Francisco Lana (or de Lana), who in 1670 crystallized the idea in his intelligent and theoretically feasible attempt to bring about lighter-than-air flight. As will be seen from Fig. 2 he planned four vacuum copper spheres to lift his craft, but did not realize that atmospheric pressure would collapse such thin globes. He never tried to build it, but left in his *Prodromo* a drawing, a description and an astonishing account of an air-raid which he saw being carried out by his aircraft.

The present writer believes he has cleared up the next point in ballooning history, but the explanatory document is a long one. The point is that another Jesuit Father, Bartholomeu de Gusmão, hit upon the hot-air idea and sent up a small balloon in Lisbon in 1709. More remarkable still is the aircraft designed by him *c.* 1709–24 (Fig. 3) of which no proper explanation survives but which is

Fig. 3. Gusmão's Aerial Ship.

obviously a hot-air balloon or airship. The popular drawing of another Gusmão aircraft sometimes reproduced in aeronautical histories is a quite different and confused idea, and again the explanation is too long to repeat here.

It was not until 1783 that the great tradition of flapping flight— gods, angels, Icarus, bird-men and so on—was joined by the reality of floating flight; the aggressive and virile symbolism linked with its passive and rotund female counterpart.

Plate 1. *The First Public Balloon Ascent, at Annonay, 1783.*

The brothers Joseph and Étienne Montgolfier, papermakers of Annonay, near Lyons, were led by reading Priestley's treatise on air to experiment with paper bags held over the kitchen fire. When

13

filled with hot air, they rose to the ceiling. The brothers decided on bigger and better bags until after a lot of experimenting they made a large linen and paper balloon, buttoned together in gores. They lit a fire of wool and straw and sent up their balloon from the market place of Annonay on 5 June 1783 and so ushered in the air age. This event led to a strange sequence. Paris soon heard of the balloon and the Academy commissioned their Professor Charles to investigate. He was a shrewd man and wasted no time on getting eye-witness accounts. He assumed (as it happened quite wrongly) that the inventor had utilized Cavendish's discovery of hydrogen in 1766, which was often known, by the way, as 'inflammable air'. He therefore set about designing a hydrogen balloon from scratch, so to speak. This small globe, of thirteen feet diameter, was sent up before an astonished multitude of spectators who had gathered in the rain on the Champ de Mars, 27 August 1783. A wag asked Benjamin Franklin, who was present, what use a balloon was. The old man, wondering about possible man-carrying craft and what would one day come of it all, turned to him and replied, 'And of what use is a new-born baby?'

A still more astonished group of peasants, later, saw a great globe descend out of the clouds and bounce on to their fields. Terrified yet inquisitive, the inhabitants of the little village of Gonesse stood gaping at this strange thing; then they poked it with a pitchfork. Punctured, the poor balloon hissed forth some of its impure hydrogen. The smell was evil, the yokels remembered their Bible, and Professor Charles's first brain child was set upon and beaten to death, and its remains then tied to the tail of a horse.

Plate 2. The First Aerial Voyage, Paris, 1783.

The Montgolfier brothers had arrived in Paris and were working hard on their new hot-air balloon which was not ready and demonstrated to the Academy until 12 September. Events then moved fast. On 19 September they succeeded in sending up another balloon carrying a sheep, duck and cock. All landed safely. Then came more experiments and the question of a human ascent. A new balloon was built and the king wanted to send up two criminals for the first flight; but Pilâtre de Rozier persuaded his Majesty to allow him to ascend with the Marquis d'Arlandes, which (after some tethered experiments) they did, on 21 November 1783, to make the first aerial voyage in history—five and a half miles in twenty-five minutes from the Château de la Muette in the Bois de Boulogne.

This truly portentous event was accompanied by a minimum of thrills, and went off smoothly. There survives a calm and detailed account written by d'Arlandes himself in a letter to M. Faujas de Saint-Fond, the first piece of aerial reporting.

All hot-air balloons came naturally to be called 'Montgolfières', just as the early hydrogen balloons became known as 'Charlières'. Balloons of both types had to be hoisted limp between two poles for filling. The Montgolfière then had a fire lit beneath the 'stage' which swelled out the envelope and another fire was attached and carried aloft in a brazier slung in the neck of the balloon. The Charlière merely needed a hose connecting the neck with the hydrogen plant, the gas being made by passing dilute sulphuric acid over iron filings.

Plate 3. *The First Hydrogen Voyage*, 1783.

Back to Professor Charles. He was a remarkable man. Foreseeing almost all the needs of ballooning he quickly designed (and the brothers Robert built) a rubberized fabric hydrogen balloon complete with net to support the basket, valve, ballast, and barometer (for height recording). With this almost modern balloon he ascended from the Tuileries on 1 December 1783 with the elder of the Robert brothers and came down safely at Nesle, twenty-seven miles away. It was the birth of proper ballooning, which flourished until this century. This plate shows the landing.

The Montgolfière continued to have a certain vogue, but the obvious superiority of the gas balloon drove it out of use except for later parachute descents in the nineteenth century where it was cheap and also did not fly far away after the parachutist had descended.

Plate 4. *The First Channel Crossing by Air*, 1785.
From a contemporary print.

Jean-Pierre Blanchard was the first, and one of the greatest, aerial showmen of all time. He did little to advance aeronautics technically, but for creating air-mindedness he had no rival and made the first ascents in many European countries and in the U.S.A. (Plate 7). He was an unpleasant creature—'a petulant little fellow, not many inches over five feet, and physically well suited for vapourish regions'. Being determined to be the first man to fly the Channel and having persuaded the American physician Dr John Jeffries to finance the trip, he did everything he could to prevent the Doctor from accompanying him, even to wearing a lead-lined belt and pretending the balloon was not big enough to support them both.

After a first-class row, patched up by the Governor of Dover Castle, they set off from the Dover cliffs on 7 January 1785, with a strangely assorted cargo including the very necessary barometer (for height) and compass, thirty pounds of ballast, flags, anchors, cork jackets, a packet of pamphlets, a bottle of brandy, some biscuits, apples, two useless silk-covered aerial oars, an equally useless rudder, and Blanchard's famous 'moulinet'—a sort of hand-operated revolving fan, quite useless, but a forerunner of the modern aeroplane propeller.

They got away safely, Jeffries being entranced with the wonderful view of the countryside behind them. The crossing was a hectic affair. The balloon appears to have been leaky, and not very well piloted at that. They could not achieve gradual ascent and descent and had to throw all their ballast: later on they began unloading the other bits and pieces, brandy and all. Just off the French coast, the position became really serious. They were on a fast down run and then everything moveable in the car had to go overboard, even to the aeronauts' clothes. It was here that the excitable Blanchard panicked and even threw his trousers overboard! The balloon started on an up-run again and they were finally deposited safely, but nearly frozen, in the forest of Guînes some twelve miles inland from Calais. They were made a great fuss of, quite rightly, and entertained as heroes for weeks afterwards by the hospitable French. The car of the balloon is still preserved in the Calais Museum.

Plate 5. Sadler and Clayfield in the Bristol Channel, 1810.
From a contemporary engraving by E. M. Jones in the Hodgson Collection.

James Sadler (1751–1828), confectioner, of Oxford, has the honour of being the first true English aeronaut. In 1784 he ascended in a

Montgolfière at Oxford before a great crowd and 'received the approbation of the whole University, to whom he gave the utmost satisfaction'. He soon took to the more practical hydrogen balloon and during his life made many ascents (with a curious interval of twenty-four years in which he apparently never went up) and on 24 September 1810, set off with a Mr William Clayfield from Bristol. Having released a parachute, with a cat suspended beneath it in a basket, they drifted over the Bristol Channel towards Cardiff. When four miles off Combe Martin, short of both gas and ballast, they came down in the sea. Fortunately it was a fairly calm day and, their balloon acting as a sail, the aeronauts spent an hour being wafted along like a ship until at last they were rescued from what was at best an uncomfortable journey, by a boat from Lynmouth, where they were landed.

Sadler had another ducking when attempting to cross the Irish Sea in 1812, but died peacefully in his bed at Oxford in 1828. One of his sons, Windham, was thrown from his balloon and killed in 1824 when making his thirty-first ascent.

Plate 6. *The First Aerial Voyage in England, 1784.*
From a contemporary engraving in the Hodgson Collection.

Vincent Lunardi, handsome secretary to the Neapolitan Embassy in London, made the first true aerial journey in England on 15 September 1784, ascending in his blue and red balloon before a huge crowd from the Artillery Ground at Moorfields. He took with him a pigeon (which escaped), a cat, a dog, a bottle of wine, a leg of chicken and some other provisions, the latter becoming inedible as they got mixed with the sand ballast! Waving his flag he passed over London to 'the most extravagant expressions of approbation and joy'. He first landed, or rather just touched down, at North Mimms, when the cat decided it had had enough and abandoned ship. Lunardi threw ballast and was up again. He finally came down at Standon, near Ware (in Hertfordshire), having covered twenty-four miles in two and a quarter hours. The flight excited great interest and Lunardi was the hero of the day. The vogue of Lunardi bonnets and garters was typical of the compliments paid him, especially by the ladies. The oars which can be seen on the car were, of course, useless, but were a common feature of early hydrogen balloons.

Lunardi made a number of other flights, but the famous Bartolozzi engraving of him ascending with Mr Biggin and the beautiful Mrs Sage was a record of a hope, not an achievement. The balloon would lift only two, so Lunardi chivalrously sent off his two guests by themselves. Neither had ever been airborne before, but they landed safely near Harrow.

Plate 7a. The First Aircraft to Crash, 1785.
Re-drawn from a contemporary print.

It was unkind of Fate to ordain that the first air pilot in the world should also become the first aerial fatality. But Pilâtre de Rozier was tragically misguided. Seeking to advance aerostation, he designed a combination balloon, with a hot-air cylinder below and a hydrogen envelope above—the 'Aero-Montgolfière' or 'Rozière'. With his companion Romain he set off on 15 June 1785 to repeat the Channel crossing; as you may guess, the hydrogen caught alight and they crashed to death near Boulogne soon after taking off.

Plate 7b. The First Aerial Journey in the U.S.A., 1793.
From the only known copy of Blanchard's contemporary account, by courtesy of the Franklin Institute and the American Philosophical Society, Philadelphia.

This historic flight was made by the Frenchman Blanchard from the yard of the old Washington Prison at Philadelphia (then the American capital) on 9 January 1793. Watched by President Washington himself and a large crowd, he ascended with a small dog and sailed off to Gloucester County, New Jersey, where he landed safely forty-six minutes later. Blanchard did not have much luck in the States. Most of the crowd for this first flight chose to remain outside the yard rather than pay two or five dollars for a close view of the take-off. Then, trying to recoup his finances, he exhibited his balloon in public and had it damaged by 'wicked people' who threw stones at it. He stayed over there two years, and the chief thing he is remembered for was sending down a cat, dog and squirrel attached to a single parachute—a cruel sport common in European ballooning at the time.

Ballooning had an exciting history in the United States during the nineteenth century and produced many famous aeronauts—among them John Wise, Charles Durant, John La Mountain and T. S. C. Lowe, of Civil War fame. By the way, the first person actually to rise in the air in America was thirteen-year-old Edward Warren, who was airborne for a few minutes beneath a hot-air balloon in Baltimore on 24 June 1784, but this cannot rank as an important event.

Plate 8. French Military Observation Balloon, 1795.

From a water-colour by N.-J. Conté in the Museum at Chalais Meudon.

Military reconnaissance from the air was first carried out from the French balloon *Entreprenant* on 2 June 1794 at Maubeuge. Napoleon formed two companies of 'aerostiers', which were of some military, and considerable psychological, value. Plate 8 shows the *Entreprenant* at the siege of Mainz in 1795. The balloons were spherical and were held captive at first with one cable, then with two; they were inflated with hydrogen made in the field. Standard equipment also included the *tent-abri*, a portable cover and wind-break which was stretched over the balloon and pegged down.

Military ballooning has been carried on, for one purpose or another, ever since. Among the many military ballooning events of the nineteenth century was the bombing of Venice in 1849 by pilotless Montgolfières with time fuzes, sent over by the Austrians; the ascents by Lowe and others in the American Civil War, 1861–63; and the dramatic balloon service out of besieged Paris, 1870–71. Captive observation balloons have been used all over the world and in practically every war to date. Until 1896 these craft were spherical, but in that year the Germans introduced the sausage balloon (*Drachen*) and started the long line of captive balloons which has ended with the barrage balloon of our own day.

Another job carried out in wartime was the dropping of propaganda leaflets, either from manned or pilotless balloons.

A curious repetition of the Venice bombing idea was seen in the recent war, when the Japanese sent some 9,000 drifting hydrogen balloons carrying bombs and incendiaries against the American west coast. They were not successful.

Plate 9. Festivities at the Coronation of Napoleon, 1804.
From a print in the Hodgson collection.

This plate is a detail of one of the finest balloon prints, drawn by
Le Cœur. The scene is the Place de la Concorde on 3 December 1804,
when Napoleon was crowned by the Pope in Paris. It is possible that
Garnerin was the pilot of the large balloon with the great eagle
decoration. The small balloons, with red and white gores, were
pilotless. In the evening of 16 December Garnerin let off a large pilotless balloon which bore an illuminated crown. This balloon caused a
great fuss, as it ultimately drifted to Italy and crashed on Nero's tomb
before finally ending up in Lake Bracciano. The obvious remarks
in the Italian newspapers about the resemblance between the two
dictators thoroughly upset Napoleon.

Plate 10. Parachutes.
Plate 10*a* from a contemporary engraving.
Plate 10*b* from a coloured lithograph by W. Lake in Hodgson Collection.

Parachutes only belong in a book on ballooning because, naturally,
it was from balloons that live drops were first made. Leonardo da
Vinci invented the parachute about 1500, but it was not until the end
of the eighteenth century that they became a practical business.
Although Blanchard made some tests it was the Frenchman André
Jacques Garnerin (1769–1825) who first made a successful drop in
Paris in 1797. As shown in Plate 10*a*, he also made the first parachute
descent in England, over North Audley Street on 21 September 1802.
The parachute with its passenger was taken up beneath a balloon (the
canopy being loose like a curtain) and on being released, the parachute
opened and came down safely. As there was no vent at the top, the
violent oscillation made poor Garnerin very sick just when he was
about to be chaired in triumph by the crowd. His niece, Eliza Garnerin,
was the first woman to make a descent (1815).

A water-colour painter named Robert Cocking witnessed
Garnerin's drop, and his indisposition, and after much thought
decided that if you inverted the parachute (Fig. 1) it would not
oscillate. Thirty-five years later, on 24 July 1837 he had made a
full-sized version of his design and (without testing it first with a

dummy) persuaded the balloonist Green to take him up suspended beneath the *Great Nassau* Balloon. Green reluctantly agreed on condition that Cocking operated his own release gear. This he did and cast off at 5,000 feet. The parachute careered down, then its ribs cracked and Cocking plunged to his death in a field near Lee Green in Kent (Plate 10*b*).

Parachute drops from balloons were a regular feature throughout the nineteenth century, both men and women doing spectacular turns at fairs and entertainments. It was also parachuting that kept alive the hot-air balloon as it was cheap to inflate and soon came down after the parachutist had cast off and its air had cooled.

Plate 11. London to Nassau, 1836.

From a lithograph in *Aeronautica* by Monck Mason (London, 1838).

The London to Nassau flight is one of the 'classic' balloon journeys of all time. It was originally suggested for testing out an improved guide (or trail) rope, but developed into a famous long-distance flight. Paid for by a Member of Parliament, Robert Hollond, who went as one of the passengers, the pilot was the famous Charles Green and the other passenger Monck Mason. They went up at midday from Vauxhall Gardens on 7 November 1836. At nightfall they were over Belgium. 'We could scarcely avoid the impression that we were cleaving our way through an interminable mass of black marble in which we were embedded, and which, solid a few inches before us, seemed to soften as we approached in order to admit us still farther within the precincts of its cold and dusky enclosure.' The scene shown is when they were over Liége, with the blast furnaces beneath them. They finally crossed the Rhine north of Coblenz, and landed in a field about eight miles from Weilberg, in the Duchy of Nassau, early in the morning of 8 November. They had covered 480 miles in eighteen hours. This remained a record for trips out of England until 1907.

Both balloon and pilot were amongst the most famous in the century. Built that same year, of 2,000 yards of crimson and white silk, the balloon was christened the *Royal Vauxhall Balloon*. After the journey to Nassau it was renamed the *Great Balloon of Nassau*.

It was in use for more than thirty-five years, being subsequently bought by another famous balloonist, Coxwell, who used it (after reconditioning) as late as 1873.

Charles Green, the pilot, was one of the outstanding balloon pilots. Born in 1785, he first went up in 1821. His five-hundredth and last ascent was in 1852. He died from heart failure in 1870 at the age of eighty-five. His two chief technical achievements were the introduction of coal gas for lifting balloons (in 1821) and the general use of the trail-rope, which had been suggested as early as 1786.

Plates 12 and 13. Ideas for Dirigibles, 1801 and 1817.

Plate 12 from *Über meine Erfindung einen Luftballon durch Adler zu regieren* by J. Kaiserer (Vienna, 1801) in the library of the Royal Aeronautical Society.
Plate 13 from a coloured engraving (1818) in the Hodgson Collection.

From the very first, the idea of making a balloon navigable was worrying the inventors. Suggestions ranged from the sensible idea of propellers, through oars and sails, to the picturesque solution of bird-traction. This last has, of course, a noble history throughout myth and legend. In ballooning the designs range from the charming harnessed pair of eagles seen here (1801) to a veritable bird galley with a team of sixteen eagles in frames suggested by Mackintosh as late as 1835.

Pauly and Egg's *Dolphin* balloon of 1816–17 must rank as 'the first serious attempt to construct a dirigible in England'. John Pauly and Durs Egg were both Swiss, the latter being gun-maker to George III. They started to build their charming monster at Knightsbridge, but it was never finished, and brought much ribaldry on the heads of the inventors. *Egg's Folly* as it was called, was to have been propelled by oars and be fitted with an interior ballonet to keep its shape. The little yellow box visible near the tail is a remarkable (indeed the first) effort to alter the trim of an airship by a movable weight.

The history of airships is a separate subject, but as it grew directly out of balloons a few words about it should be said here. The modern airship with elongated envelope, propellers, and rudder was first envisaged in some remarkable drawings by the French officer Meusnier as early as 1784, but the craft was never built. The first practical airship was made by the French engineer Giffard in 1852, with a steam-driven propeller. But he could not exercise complete control of it. The first really successful craft, *La France*, was constructed by two other Frenchmen, Renard and Krebs, in 1884. It was propelled by an electrically driven airscrew. After that the airship as we know it developed rapidly. The first Zeppelin, by the way, was born in 1900. It should be noted here that to this day all airship pilots must first qualify as free balloon pilots as engine trouble in a dirigible may turn it quickly into a free aerostat.

Plate 14. Death of Madame Blanchard, 1819.

From an early nineteenth-century woodcut.

On the evening of 7 July 1819, a happy crowd of Parisians thronged the Tivoli Gardens. The main event was to be a firework display from a balloon piloted by the popular Madame Blanchard. Ascending to music and the light of Bengal fire, a rain of gold cascades from the car; then she sends down a bomb of silver rain on a parachute. There is another burst of flame and the crowd applauds. But they do not realize that it is the balloon itself which has caught alight. Madame Blanchard does not lose her head. As the gas burns and she falls faster, the fire is almost choked and there is some chance for her. She throws ballast to check the fall as the balloon is carried low over some houses. But the car hits the roof of a house in the rue de Provence. She is thrown into the street and dies of a broken neck.

Small, ugly and nervous, Madame Blanchard was the first professional woman aeronaut, and made a success of it. She was the wife of the famous 'Cross-Channel' Blanchard and first went solo in 1805. She hated all noise (incidentally riding in carriages was another terror for her) and often used to go up at night and stay there till dawn. She became a great favourite and, among many flights, made the ascent at Napoleon's marriage festivities in 1810. Her most serious rival as a woman pilot was Eliza Garnerin, niece of the parachutist (see Plate 10a), who was the first woman to come down in a parachute, in 1815. Madame Blanchard never took to this form of aerial sport. Like many other aeronauts she lived a dangerous life and died in harness. She was the first of a line of women aeronauts popular throughout the nineteenth century, and the true ancestor of the woman pilot of today.

The technical reason for her balloon, which was very small, catching alight was the gas expanding as the balloon rose and blowing off down the open neck where it was caught either by the fireworks themselves or by the lighted wand used for touching them off.

Plate 15. An Alarming Experience in Gypson's Balloon, 6 July 1847.

From a contemporary woodcut in the *Illustrated London News.*

You may well ask what happens to aeronauts when a balloon bursts. First of all, balloons seldom *do* burst. Secondly, there is a way out, first used by the American John Wise. The incident shown here was one of the first in this country, and provided the standard cure for later accidents. The famous balloonist Coxwell had ascended from Vauxhall Gardens on 6 July 1847 with Gypson (in the latter's balloon) together with two other passengers, to give a firework display. They had already let off some of the fireworks successfully when a thunderstorm came on and they went up to 7,000 feet, at which height the balloon burst—probably owing to over-rapid expansion of gas and a weak envelope. They immediately began hurtling down. Coxwell, who was sitting in the hoop, immediately ordered everything movable to be thrown overboard; he himself, with great presence of mind, cut the neck-line with his knife. The neck-line loosely secures the neck to the hoop to prevent it flapping about and snarling the valve-line when there is only a little gas left after a long journey. With the line cut, the whole envelope was driven by the air up into the top of the net and so acted as a parachute. They came down, badly shaken but quite safe, in the newly constructed Belgrave Road, Pimlico.

Plate 16. The Death of Thomas Harris, 1824.

From an aquatint after a drawing made on the spot by T. T. Dales, in the Hodgson Collection.

'The Science of Aerostation', wrote Harris, 'has lately fallen into much decay, and been the subject of ridicule through the total want of invention.' What worried him was the lack of means to empty the balloon rapidly on landing and so prevent it being dragged all over the countryside, which often happened. Not being fated to think of the ripping panel, he designed a large valve in the crown of the balloon which was really one valve within another. For ordinary purposes you pulled open the small one; for quick deflation both together. It was obviously open to human error and the error was made over Beddington Park (near Croydon) on 25 May 1824, when he pulled the wrong cord. He had ascended with a Miss Stocks from the Haymarket, and the balloon was suddenly seen to descend violently. It fell on an oak tree, killing Harris and injuring the lady. The fact of Miss Stocks's survival gave rise to a story of great chivalry which later became very popular in France and which may perhaps be true. The story goes that Harris, seeing there was no hope of arresting the fall, deliberately jumped out, so that the balloon would be sufficiently lightened to bring down Miss Stocks with a comparatively small bump.

Plate 17. Rural Sports: Balloon Hunting, 1811.
From a print in the Hodgson Collection.

This delightful caricature by Thomas Rowlandson commemorates, perhaps, a common sport in the early and 'middle' periods of ballooning—that of chasing the balloon by road or on horseback over the countryside, and greeting the aeronaut upon landing. Dr John Sheldon set the fashion by following Lunardi on his historic flight from London on 15 September 1784 (see Plate 6). The particular scene represented here, however, is a fantasy of wishful thinking. We do not know whether the party in the foreground is taking part in the familiar balloon hunt or whether they have merely been frightened by the goings-on in the background.

A balloon, complete with customary flags, has evidently witnessed an argument amongst its passengers or a panic on the part of the lady. Anyway, she decides to make an umbrella descent and is in full flight at the moment when a flock of birds is passing—a target for the sportsman on the tower. Or has a Regency eccentric, seeing a balloon approach his estate, hastened to the top of his 'folly' to take a crack at the intruder, only to experience even greater satisfaction (such eccentrics often being misogynists) at finding an additional target in the generous proportions of the lady parachutist?

Plate 18. *An Unwilling Juvenile Aeronaut*, 1843.
From a contemporary woodcut in *L'Illustration*.

The French aeronaut Kirsch, celebrated for his aerostatic mis-adventures, was about to ascend in a Montgolfière at Nantes on 16 July 1843. The fire had been lit and the balloon, having filled out, tugged itself free of the ground crew. Unfortunately its anchor, dragging along the ground, caught in the trousers of twelve-year-old Master Guérin and bore him off. He managed to clutch the rope and hang on, crying out in terror as the balloon rose to 300 metres. The boy stuck it out for a quarter of an hour, when the hot air cooled and the balloon started to descend. He let go from some height and was caught by the excited crowd which had pursued this unfortunate and unwilling aeronaut.

Plate 19. *An Equestrian Ascent by Poitevin*, 1850.
From a contemporary woodcut in the *Illustrated London News*.

The showmen of ballooning welcomed any new method of draw-ing a crowd. It was Testu Brissy who started the cruel sport of equestrian ascents in 1798, and he was followed by Poitevin and Margat, the latter going up on the back of his stag *Coco*. Poitevin is seen in this Plate ascending from the Paris Hippodrome on 14 July 1850 on his pony *Blanche*. It is interesting to find Madame Poitevin being haled before our courts and prevented, on the ground of cruelty to animals, from going up as Europa on the Bull when she and her husband visited England in 1852. There were also protests (not from the same source) at Madame Poitevin making parachute drops, but she was rightly allowed to risk her own neck.

Plate 20. *Shooting Stars*, 1870.

One of the fine coloured lithographs in the second edition of *Travels in the Air* (1871) edited by James Glaisher. They were drawn by Albert Tissandier to illustrate some of the remarkable skyscapes which balloonists enjoyed.

Plate 21. *Balloon Mirage*, 1870.

Another of the Tissandier lithographs. The phenomenon of what meteorologists call a 'glory' was described to Tissandier by the French aeronaut Flammarion, who saw it on 15 April 1868. Familiar to mountaineers, it was the first time that such a spectacle had been viewed from a balloon. One had hoped for some impressive rhetoric by the witness, but there is none.

Plate 22. *Victorian Altitude Record*, 1862.
From the woodcut in *Travels in the Air*, edited by J. Glaisher (1871).

This well-known picture has always typified the adventure of ballooning, since its publication in 1871. The incident itself was a genuine enough achievement, but cannot be taken at its face value. James Glaisher, F.R.S., was taken up on a number of meteorological flights by the famous aeronaut Coxwell. On one of these ascents from Wolverhampton on 5 September 1862, Glaisher passed out for a time and Coxwell nearly did, but they landed safe and sound in the end. The picture shows Coxwell in the hoop, his hands frozen, pulling the valve line with his teeth whilst Glaisher slumps unconscious in the basket. Glaisher was obviously affected by the height and possibly had faulty instruments as well. At any rate his account of the flight was not only inconsistent, but he says he passed out at 29,000 feet and the balloon rose to at least 36,000 feet before descending. Modern pilots use oxygen masks at heights above 15,000 feet, but have occasionally been known to fly without them around 24,000 feet. Glaisher may therefore have got to 19,000 feet, or a bit higher, but his own claim is nonsense. The facts about Coxwell are also curious. The valve-line was just out of easy reach and he was unwise enough to take off his gloves, get on to the side of the basket and grasp the icy hoop—he did not get up into the rigging as shown. He managed to fumble the end of the line out of its containing bag and then take it in his teeth. But it was a good effort and certainly a record flight.

Plate 23. *The 'Géant'*, 1863.
From a contemporary woodcut in the *Illustrated London News*.

This ill-fated monster—the Paris press called her a 'chimerical project'—was built for Nadar in 1863 by Eugene Godard. She held 210,000 cubic feet of gas and had a two-storied basket which could hold a dozen passengers. The first ascent took place from Paris,

4 October 1863, and soon ended near Meaux. The second, on 18 October, ended in one of the most publicized accidents of the century. Mistaking a cloud bank for the sea the pilot brought her down in a high wind in Hanover, after a 400-mile journey, and the unfortunate passengers were dragged crashing through the countryside, demolishing everything in their path. The bruises were many and serious, but not fatal. Nadar made some more experiments and even brought over the *Géant* and exhibited it in the Crystal Palace (1863–4) in order to raise funds, but the public soon became tired of such a business which was neither good showmanship nor good sport.

Plate 24. Children's Balloons at Cremorne Gardens, 1859.
From a contemporary woodcut in the *Illustrated London News*.

This 'juvenile fête and balloon race' is typical of the toyshop appeal of the balloon. As with railways, so with balloons—the appeal of the model has lasted from the earliest aerostatic toys in 1783 till today.

Plate 25. The 'Zénith' Tragedy, 1875.
From a popular contemporary print.

The tragedy of the French balloon *Zénith* is somewhat parallel to the famous Coxwell and Glaisher ascent of 1862, except that the Englishmen survived the ordeal. The *Zénith*, carrying MM. G. Tissandier, Crocé-Spinelli and Sivel, rose from Paris on 15 April 1875 on a scientific high altitude flight. They carried primitive oxygen apparatus, but did not use it properly, and all three passed out at about 25,000 feet. Tissandier came to on the way down, but the others were dead, and the balloon made a crash landing at Ciron (Indre). They had been up four and a half hours. The tragedy caused a great sensation in France and the two aeronauts were given an official and impressive funeral. By the way, the elaborate tomb in the Père Lachaise Cemetery is quite worth a visit.

Plate 26. Marriage in a Balloon, 1874.

American showmanship was bound sooner or later to think of staging a balloon marriage, just as later on we were to hear of aeroplane marriages. We show two contemporary woodcuts, one of a scene in Cincinnati (Plate 26) and one in New York (1865) (on title page). Both are quite charming period pieces.

Sixty-six balloons left Paris during the siege of 1870–1, and they go to make one of the great chapters of balloon history. They left Paris at first by day; then, after some near misses by Prussian shells and bullets, night ascents became the rule. Their jobs were to evacuate 'V.I.P.s' (they took, excluding pilots, over a hundred, including Gambetta); transport mail (nine tons went in all); take out carrier pigeons (over four hundred, of which only fifty-seven got back) and five trained dogs (which never returned). Of the sixty-six balloons, fifty-nine succeeded in landing in friendly territory, five fell into Prussian hands, and two disappeared altogether, which almost certainly came down in the sea. There were exciting escapes and adventures; and a remarkable feature of the business was the carrying back into Paris, by the fifty-seven pigeons, of some hundred thousand messages on micro-film, one of its earliest applications. Another job carried out by the aeronauts was the dropping of propaganda leaflets, despite the poor chance of success amongst the Prussians.

One of the most astonishing events in the history of exploration took place in 1930, when a whaling party stumbled into the ice-covered remains of the Andrée Polar expedition of 1897 on White Island, Spitsbergen. Andrée and two companions had attempted to drift across the North Pole in the balloon *Eagle*. They left Danes Island on 11 July 1897 and, except for a few routine messages dropped in buoys and one carrier-pigeon, were never heard of again. When discovered by a million-to-one chance the skeletons and the entire equipment of the expedition, including complete diaries, were found miraculously preserved, even to ink in the fountain pens and paraffin in the Primus stove. The crowning miracle was the development of Andrée's photographs after more than thirty years. One of them is reproduced in this Plate and shows the *Eagle* stranded on the ice, immediately after she was forced down by a heavy coating of frozen mist.

Plate 29. The Gordon Bennett Race, 1926.

From a photograph (copyright Central Press Photos Ltd.).

The Gordon Bennett Race is one of the few sporting events that have kept ballooning alive over the years, except for the war periods. It was founded in 1906 by James Gordon Bennett (1841–1918) the son of the founder of the *New York Herald*. Gordon Bennett inherited the newspaper, but was far better known to the world as a promoter of sporting events especially in yachting, motoring and aeronautics. The first balloon race started from the Tuileries, Paris, and was won with a flight of 402 miles by the American Lt F. P. Lahm who landed at Whitby in Yorkshire. This Plate shows the 'line-up' for the race at Antwerp in 1926. The Gordon Bennett is a distance race, to the farthest point from the start. The two other popular balloon sports were the point-to-point competitions where the winner was the one who descended nearest to a prearranged spot; and the hare-and-hounds, where the 'hounds' have to chase and land as near as possible to the 'hare'.

Plate 30. The Perils of Ballooning, 1908.

From the *Graphic*, 30 May 1908. Courtesy *The Sphere*.

The Aero Club (later Royal Aero Club) was founded in 1901 and within a short time ballooning became a fashionable sport for both men and women. The meetings at Ranelagh and Hurlingham were miniature Ascots, and the year 1908 saw the high peak of the balloon renaissance. The decline of ballooning began when Europe first really became aeroplane-conscious in 1909 and the sport almost disappeared in 1914. This drawing by C. H. Taffs is another perfect period piece, its sub-title being 'Drifting seaward, something wrong with the valve'. The masher in the hoop is trying to see what's wrong, whilst the others look understandably apprehensive.

Plate 31. World Altitude Record, 1935.

It is a matter of lively satisfaction to balloonatics that the highest point ever reached by man was in a balloon. On 11 November 1935 two American army captains, O. A. Anderson and A. W. Stevens took off in the *Explorer II* from the 'Stratobowl', near Rapid City, in South Dakota and reached the great height of 72,395 feet (13.7 miles). The colossal balloon, filled with helium, had a capacity of 3,700,000 cubic feet—forty-six times the size of a big sporting balloon —and took up a circular metal gondola containing the aeronauts and a large assortment of instruments for scientific research. Owing to the space necessary for gas expansion the envelope only filled out to the shape of a sphere when it was in the upper regions. Stevens and Anderson had already made one stratosphere attempt in the *Explorer I* (in 1934) and reached over 60,000 feet when the balloon burst owing to a faulty ripping panel, and they had to bale out! Both flights were sponsored by the National Geographic Society and the U.S. Army, by whose courtesy this remarkable photograph is included. It shows *Explorer II* just before the rip-cord was pulled to land her some twelve miles south of White Lake, South Dakota, after a flight lasting eight and a quarter hours.

Plate 32. Cruikshank's Taxi-Balloons, 1825.
From a print in the Hodgson Collection.

This caricature is the most famous of the endless skits on balloons which provided a reliable humorous standby for a century and a quarter. The couple on the left are just embarking for the City at a shilling fare.

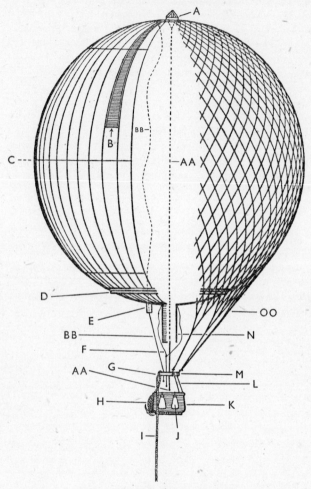

Fig. 4. Cut-away diagram of a balloon.
The vertical gores (left) are not shown beneath the net (right),
for clarity.

THE ANATOMY OF BALLOONING

A BALLOON is in essence a thin envelope filled with a gas lighter than air which supports, by means of an enveloping net, a basket for the crew. The balloon, along with its load, must together weigh less than the corresponding volume of surrounding air which it displaces. It will then rise like a cork. As the atmosphere becomes less dense the gas in the balloon blows off through the always open neck beneath, thus keeping the balloon at the same pressure as the surrounding air. It will go on ascending until the weight of balloon, gas and load becomes equal to the corresponding volume of the surrounding air, when it will therefore rest in equilibrium. To rise further you drop ballast (generally sand) and the process starts all over again. To descend the valve is opened, gas escapes, and the balloon falls. That is a much simplified description of balloon flight.

There are three gases used in ballooning, and from their weights it will be seen how different are their lifting powers. At sea-level air weighs 76 lb. per 1,000 cubic feet, coal gas about 36 lb., helium 10.5 lb. and hydrogen only 5.3 lb. Hydrogen is by far the lightest, but very inflammable; helium is best as it does not burn, but is very expensive; and coal gas is inflammable but much the cheapest and so, since its introduction for ballooning in 1821, the most commonly used.

On page 32 is a cut-away drawing of a typical 80,000 cubic feet sporting balloon such as was popular in the early years of this century. Most conspicuous is the spherical envelope (C) made of treated silk, linen or other materials, and made up of sections called *gores*. The envelope has three main openings; first, the *valve* (A) in the crown, which is kept closed by springs and can only be opened by the *valve-line* (AA) which simply hangs down inside the envelope and out through the large open *neck* (N), the other main opening. The balloon is filled through its neck (unless there is a separate filling pipe) which is connected with the gas hose, but the neck is left open through-out the flight so that when the balloon rises the expanding gas can blow off harmlessly (it can be very smelly for the crew) without bursting the envelope. The third opening, only used when landing, is the *ripping-panel* (B) which is made to pull away inside the envelope by the *ripping-line* (BB) shown here for clarity as a wavy line. It is actually passed first, for safety, through two or three breaking straps inside, near the crown, and then hangs down like the valve-line; but it is always kept well away from its neighbour: it is led through its own small *sleeve* (E), is dyed bright red to avoid tragic confusion, and coiled in a red bag attached to the hoop (M). With the ripping-panel torn out, the balloon deflates in a matter of seconds.

A small but important item is the *neck-line* (F) which is a bridle and cord attached to the bottom of the envelope by the neck. In flight it is tied to the hoop (M) and its main job is to hold down the bottom of the envelope when it is flabby through loss of gas, and so prevent the snarling of valve and ripping-lines. In an emergency it is immediately cut and the envelope then floats up into the top of the net and forms a parachute (see Plate 15). Another oddment is the *drip-flap* (D) which leads rain and moisture off the balloon and clear of the crew.

Covering the envelope is the *net* whose function is to support the basket and distribute the weight evenly over the surface of the balloon. The cording is reduced first to the *crows' feet* (OO) then to the leading lines which are toggled on to the *hoop*, or ring (M), from which the *basket* (K) is suspended by the *car lines* (L). The basket was for a long time known as the 'car'.

Also toggled on to the hoop are two stout ropes, the most important of which is the *trail rope* (I), introduced by Green in 1828. This is a rope 250 feet long (for this size balloon) increasing in diameter near the free end, which at low altitudes trails on land or water and acts as automatic ballast according to how much of its weight is deposited on the ground. The trail rope is generally let down soon after the take-off and is, incidentally, too heavy to pull up again. There were apt to be complaints by farmers about this useful equipment and on at least one occasion peaceable inhabitants were struck by it! The other rope ends in a *grapnel* (H), but when the ripping panel made its very late appearance in Europe (invented by Wise in the U.S.A. in 1839) the grapnel, which could make life very uncomfortable, was often dispensed with. Both trail and grapnel ropes must be fixed in line with the ripping-panel so that when the balloon lands the torn-out panel remains uppermost and not smothered by the envelope.

The main instruments and controls essential to the pilot are the valve-line (kept coiled in a white bag attached to the hoop) the ripping-line, the neck-line, bags of ballast (generally of 20 or 30 lb. each) (J), an altimeter (barometer) for height recording, a statoscope for rate of fall or climb, and a compass. In the old days bits of paper or streamers were used instead of a statoscope, to show if you were going up or down. In practice a number of other odds and ends were taken, as well as bags for the balloon itself and the valve; this latter equipment was collectively called the 'splosh'. The envelope and equipment were packed into the basket for the homeward journey.

When the balloon was inflated, kept down by bags hooked on to the rigging, the basket was attached and the crew went on board. Ballast bags were then removed until the ground crew were able to hold her down easily by hand. She was thus tried for lift, or weighed off, and (according to the amount of wind and local obstacles) a further amount of ballast was removed to give a good initial lift, whilst the ground crew still hung on; 20 lb. was all right for a calm day, 50 lb. for a windy one. Then the neck, which was tied up until take-off, was 'broken' by a slip knot and the command given 'Let go'. If the day was warm the gas, having come cold from the mains, would have heated up in the envelope after inflation and when the neck was broken would blow off. This 'false lift' was equal to about one bag of ballast.

Once in the air the pilot has two major problems—what the sun is doing and what the wind is doing. The sun expands the gas quickly; a passing cloud will reverse the process; you can ballast up through a cloud and the moisture (like rain) will add to the weight only to be evaporated, and the gas rapidly heated, by the sun after you have emerged; and so on. All this is quite apart from the natural expansion of gas due to reduced atmospheric pressure.

Balloon flight, unless expertly directed, tends to be a series of ups and downs. This is due to the balloon overshooting its theoretical equilibrium point on an up-run and becoming too heavy; whereupon it starts a down-run and gathers momentum until checked by throwing ballast. The longer you wait to throw, the more you have to throw. As one of the ballooning slogans is 'conserve ballast' the experienced pilot will do all he can to keep near the height he desires by immediately correcting a down-run. Even a handful of sand is effective when near equilibrium. It can be seen that in practice the valve is often not used at all until landing.

As for wind, the better meteorologist you are, so are you the better pilot, as selecting the wind currents for your direction is half the battle. Small sounding balloons are often let off before an ascent in order to observe the various wind currents.

Ballooning at night is the easiest for the pilot, as he can keep almost continually in equilibrium owing to even temperature in and outside the balloon. Silent night flight has also its own spectacular beauties.

There are three ways of landing a balloon. In any case, having chosen a suitable area ahead, the descent should be properly checked at about 500 feet from the ground. If there is very little wind you can valve right down and keep the valve open to deflate. If there is a fair wind blowing, it is best to valve down slowly to below 25 feet and then rip. For quick landing the grapnel can be dropped before ripping. Standing orders to the crew for landing are to bend knees, grab the side of the basket or car lines (never the hoop) and stay in the basket until deflation is advanced enough to make it impossible for the lightened balloon to set off again.

In the old ballooning days, when no ripping device was available, perilous landings were common; and aeronauts used to find themselves dumped in a variety of topographical features from the ocean itself to trees, haystacks and, of course, nice green fields when they were lucky.

The attraction of ballooning, apart from the spectator's attitude to showmanship, is the experience of smooth and silent flight, with superb sky- and landscapes. No motion is experienced in balloon flight, as the balloon goes at the same speed as the wind. Therefore the ground and clouds seem to be moving past, approaching or receding from the balloon, and this peculiarity of free aerostatic flight has been commented on by nearly every aeronaut since the first flight.

To round off the record here are a few words on etymology. The word 'balloon' comes, of course, from 'ball'. In Florio's Dictionary (1598) the Italian 'ballone' is translated as 'a great ball, a ballone to play at with braces, a footeball'. Then in 1626 one finds 'windblowne balones ... tossed this way and that way, some tyme with the foote, sometyme with the hand'. It was therefore natural that the word should be taken over and modified, especially as the first balloons were very much like large footballs. The word 'balloon' was introduced in English in the first year of flight, 1783. A balloon is an aerostat (*aēr*—air; *sta*—stand), a lighter-than-air craft as opposed to an aerodyne, heavier-than-air craft. In the eighteenth century balloons were also called 'aerostats', 'aerostatic globes' and other variants, and 'aerostation' was used for what is now technically 'aerostatics'. American usage shows only a few variants. For example they call the hoop the 'load-ring', the neck the 'appendix', and the trail-rope the 'drag-rope'.

Fig. 5. Dragging.

A BALLOONING DATE LIST

1513 Leonardo da Vinci's hot-air toys.

1670 Lana publishes his *Prodromo* in which he describes and illustrates his Flying Ship.

1709 Gusmão sends up a hot-air balloon and designs other aircraft.

1766 Henry Cavendish discovers hydrogen.

1782 Montgolfier brothers' first hot-air experiments with paper bags (Nov.).

1783 The Montgolfiers give first public demonstration at Annonay (5 June).

1783 First hydrogen balloon sent up from Paris (27 Aug.).

1783 The Montgolfier 'animal' ascent at Versailles (19 Sept.).

1783 First aerial voyage in history, by de Rozier and d'Arlandes at Paris (21 Nov.).

1783 First voyage in a hydrogen balloon, by Charles and Robert at Paris (1 Dec.).

1784 Ascent of balloon *Le Flesselle* at Lyons. The largest hot-air balloon ever made (19 Jan.).

1784 The first woman to fly (Madame Thible) ascends as a passenger at Lyons (4 June).

1784 First aerial voyage in England, by Lunardi (15 Sept.).

1784 Sadler (first English aeronaut) makes first ascent (4 Oct.).

1784 First scientific observations from a balloon, by Dr Jeffries and Blanchard (in England) (30 Nov.).

1785 First Channel crossing, by Blanchard and Jeffries (7 Jan.).

1785 The first aerial fatality (de Rozier and Romain, near Boulogne) (15 June).

1785 Biggin and Mrs Sage (the first Englishwoman) ascend from London (29 June).

1793 First aerial voyage in U.S.A. by Blanchard (9 Jan.).

1794 Balloons first used for military observation, by the French at Maubeuge (2 June).

1797 First parachute descent, by Garnerin, at Paris (22 Oct.).

1797 Equestrian ascents by Testu-Brissy at Paris (Nov.).

1802 First parachute descent in England, by Garnerin (21 Sept.).

1804 Scientific ascents by Gay-Lussac and Biot at Paris.

1821 Green's first ascent. He introduces coal gas for the first time on this occasion (19 July).

1836 The *Vauxhall* balloon flies from London to Weilburg (Nassau)— 480 miles in 18 hours (7–8 Nov.).

1837 Cocking's fatal parachute descent (24 July).

1839 The American John Wise invents the ripping panel.

1844 Coxwell's first ascent (19 Aug.).

38

1849 First bombing raid in history—bombs attached to pilotless hot-air balloons sent by the Austrians over Venice.

1849 Alps first crossed, by Arban from Marseilles to Turin (2–3 Sept.).

1850 Barral and Bixio make scientific ascent from Paris.

1858 The first aerial photograph, taken by Nadar at Paris.

1859 American balloonist John Wise makes record flight from St. Louis to Henderson, N.Y. (809 miles in 19 hours 50 minutes) (2 July).

1861–3 Balloons used for observation in the American Civil War.

1862 Coxwell and Glaisher's high altitude flight (5 Sept.).

1863 The *Géant* catastrophe (in Hanover) (19 Oct.).

1866 Foundation of the Aeronautical Society (later Royal) in London.

1868 First aeronautical exhibition in England (Crystal Palace) (June).

1870–1 66 balloons leave besieged Paris.

1873 Donaldson attempts to cross the Atlantic from New York, but soon descends (6 Oct.).

1874 Monsieur and Madame Duruof rescued at sea after cross-Channel attempt from Calais (31 Aug.).

1875 The *Zénith* tragedy (France) (15 April).

1878 Giffard constructs his giant captive balloon for the Paris Exhibition of 1878.

1879 John Wise drowned in Lake Michigan (29 Sept.).

1880 Balloon Society of Great Britain founded. Lasted about ten years.

1890 Balloon Section formed in the Royal Engineers.

1892 Small pilot balloons first made to carry meteorological instruments (used ever since).

1896 Germans introduce the elongated balloon (*Drachen*) for observation.

1897 Andrée starts on his fatal North Pole flight (11 July).

1901 Aero Club (later Royal) of Great Britain founded (Sept.).

1901 Mediterranean crossed by de la Vaulx from Toulon to Algeria (13 Oct.).

1906 First Gordon Bennett balloon race (Paris) (30 Sept.).

1913 Duration record of 87 hours set up by H. Kaulen (Dec.).

1914 Distance record of 1,890 miles set up by H. Berliner from Bitterfeld to Kirgischan (Urals) (Feb.).

1914–18 Kite balloons used for observation by all Powers. Balloon barrage proposed and experimented with.

1931 The Belgian Professor Piccard makes first stratosphere flight from Augsburg: reaches 9·5 miles.

1935 Balloon *Explorer II* creates world's height record—72,395 feet (13.7 miles) with U.S. Captains Stevens and Anderson, over South Dakota, U.S.A. (11 Nov.).

1939–45 Balloon barrages and propaganda balloons used. Japanese use drifting bomb-dropping balloons.

A SHORT BOOK LIST

AERONAUTICA ILLUSTRATA (The Norman Collection). 10 vols., in the Patent Office Library.

ANDRÉE (S. A.). *The Andrée Diaries.* London, 1931.

BREWER (G.). *Ballooning, etc.* 11 ed. London, 1940.

BREWER (G.). *Fifty Years of Flying.* London, 1946.

BRUEL (F.-L.). *Histoire aéronautique par les monuments ... des origines à* 1830. Paris, 1901. (See also La Vaulx.)

CAVALLO (T.). *The History and Practice of Aerostation.* London, 1785.

COXWELL (H.). *My Life and Ballooning Experiences.* 2 series. London, 1887 and 1889.

DAVY (M. J. B.). *Lighter-than-Air Craft.* (Science Museum Handbooks.) London, 1934.

DOLLFUS (C.) and BOUCHER (H.). *Histoire de l'aéronautique.* Paris, 1932.

FONVIELLE (W. de). *Adventures in the Air.* London, 1877.

GLAISHER (J.). *Travels in the Air.* London, 1871.

GRAND-CARTERET (J.). *La conquête de l'air vue par l'image* (1495–1909). Paris, 1910.

HODGSON (J. E.). *The History of Aeronautics in Great Britain.* London, 1924.

LA VAULX (Comte de). *L'aéronautique des origines à* 1922. Paris, 1922. (Supplement to BRUEL.)

LECORNU (J.). *La navigation aérienne.* Paris, 1903.

MARION (F.). *Wonderful Balloon Ascents.* London, 1870.

MARSH (W. Lockwood). *Aeronautical Prints and Drawings.* London, 1924.

MASON (T. Monck). *Aeronautica.* London, 1838.

MILBANK (J.). *The First Century of Flight in America.* Princeton, 1943.

SIRCOS (A.) and PALLIER (T.). *Histoire des ballons, etc.* Paris, 1876.

TISSANDIER (G.). *Histoire des ballons, etc.* 2 vols. Paris, 1887–90.

TURNOR (C. Hatton). *Astra Castra.* London, 1865.

U.S. WAR DEPARTMENT. *Theory of Ballooning.* Washington, D.C., 1940.

UPSON (R. H.). *Free and Captive Balloons.* New York, 1926.

WAR OFFICE. *Manual of Military Ballooning.* London, 1896.

WILKINSON (S.). *Lighter than Air.* London, 1939.

I. THE FIRST PUBLIC BALLOON ASCENT. ANNONAY, 1783.

2. THE FIRST AERIAL VOYAGE. PARIS, 1783

3. THE FIRST HYDROGEN VOYAGE. 1783.

4. THE FIRST CHANNEL CROSSING BY AIR. 1785.

5. SADLER AND CLAYFIELD IN THE BRISTOL CHANNEL. 1810.

6. THE FIRST AERIAL VOYAGE IN ENGLAND. 1784.

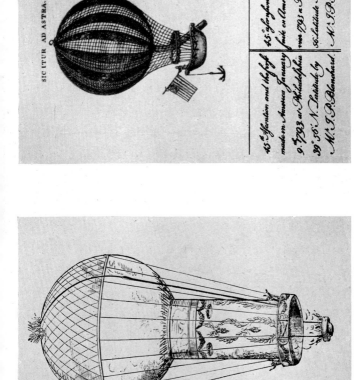

SIC ITUR AD ASTRA.

The *Ascension* and the *first voyage* made in America January 9, 1793 at Philadelphia 39° 56′ N. Latitude by Mr. J. P. Blanchard

45° Longitude. L'experience fait en Amerique le 9 Jan. 1793 à Philadelphia 56′ Latitude N. par Mr J. P. Blanchard.

7b. THE FIRST AERIAL JOURNEY IN THE U.S.A. 1793.

7a. THE FIRST AIRCRAFT TO CRASH. 1785.

8. FRENCH MILITARY OBSERVATION BALLOON. 1795.

12. KAISERER'S SUGGESTION FOR A DIRIGIBLE BALLOON. 1801.

II. LONG-DISTANCE RECORD: LONDON TO NASSAU. 1836.

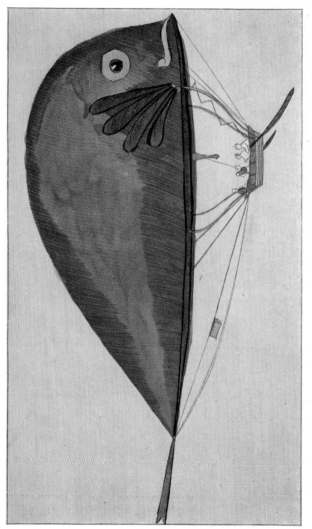

13. PAULY AND EGG'S 'DOLPHIN' DIRIGIBLE. 1816–17.

14. DEATH OF MADAME BLANCHARD. 1819.

15. AN ALARMING EXPERIENCE IN GYPSON'S BALLOON. 1847.

16. THE DEATH OF THOMAS HARRIS. 1824.

17. RURAL SPORTS: BALLOON HUNTING. 1811.

18. AN UNWILLING JUVENILE AERONAUT. 1843.

19. AN EQUESTRIAN ASCENT BY POITEVIN. 1850.

20. SHOOTING STARS SEEN FROM A BALLOON. 1870.

21. THE MIRAGE SEEN FROM A BALLOON. 1870.

22. VICTORIAN ALTITUDE RECORD. 1862.

23. THE 'GÉANT'. 1863.

24. CHILDREN'S BALLOONS AT CREMORNE GARDENS. 1859.

25. THE 'ZÉNITH' TRAGEDY. 1875.

26. MARRIAGE IN A BALLOON, CINCINNATI. 1874.

27. ESCAPE FROM PARIS. 1870.

28. ANDRÉE'S BALLOON ON THE ICE. 1897.

29. THE GORDON BENNETT RACE. 1926.

30. THE PERILS OF BALLOONING. 1908.

31. WORLD ALTITUDE RECORD. 1935.

32. CRUIKSHANK'S TAXI-BALLOONS. 1825.